Sacred Medicine Integration:

A Companion Journal Supporting Ceremonial Medicine Experiences

By

Mayra Aceves, Jonathan Anderson,
Melissa Drake, and Eden Rincon

Published by Uncorped Influence

978-1-7346543-9-4 Paperback

Printed in the United States of America

For those called to do the work

Sacred Medicine Integration

We've personally used these tools and found them to be helpful and effective. Here are some specific comments related to strategic visioning and journaling for integration:

"Having these questions and prompts for before and after ceremonial experiences is absolutely brilliant! I can clearly see how there's thought and heart and spirit into the questions and how important it is to have these prompts to completely integrate the medicine and to also go back and witness the healing experienced through the medicine. (The questions) are actually nothing short of genius! This process helps one to understand the energy of ceremony so much more. Integration is such a process and everyone's process is individually unique and essential to the medicine. There is no wrong or right process, but having this guide as a form of documentation for one's self and as a self-promise for accountability is so beautiful."
—Ceremonial Plant Medicine Practitioner Jonathan Anderson

"We are reflections of our state. Therefore, strategic visioning has allowed me to build my mental muscle and have breakthrough thinking, while creating shifts of opportunity."
—Integration Mentor Mayra Aceves

"Because I'm a writer, I know the power of writing and have used it extensively for healing purposes. Having the prompts really documented my experience. Reading the answers puts me right back

into the experience of healing and is readily available at will."
—Integration Mentor Melissa Drake

"Trabajamos para trabajar." (We work to work.)
— Ceremonial Plant Medicine Practitioner Eden Rincon

DISCLAIMER: The collaborative authors do not provide medical advice, nor are they medical professionals, licensed therapists, or counselors. They are guides who believe in the power of self-discovery through ethically sourced plant medicines. They respect and honor tribal lineage. All information provided is for educational purposes and must not be considered legal or medical advice. Claims regarding the effectiveness of medicines and results achieved are anecdotal and based on personal experiences, observations, and reported claims. All sacred medicine and ceremonial experiences should be undertaken with great care and discretion.

Table of Contents

Introduction

Message from Melissa Drake: My first experience with plant medicine was intense and enlightening. In January of 2020, around 40 people gathered to do Kambo on a beautiful Saturday morning in Southern California. I recall being surprised to see so many people willing to spend the time, the money, and purposefully go through purging in the name of healing. When going around the room setting intentions, one man mentioned his reason for being there stating, "A better me is better for everyone." I loved the idea of that and felt right at home among like-minded people who went to such great lengths to improve their life experience—not only for themselves, but also for everyone they came into contact with. Quite honestly, I was in awe and grateful to be invited by my new friend, Mayra.

Next came the actual ceremony. Almost instantly, we went from talking about intentions to aggressive collective purging. It was unnerving and sacred at the same time. As the effects of the medicine wore off, the ceremony participants chatted and shared snacks.

Then, we left to go home.

Within the span of a few hours, I went from having a profound sacred medicine experience, to returning to my regular life. Something about the lack of processing for the ceremony experience definitely felt off for me.

Having just completed a comprehensive NLP training program, and being an author who uses writing to gain perspective and process emotion, I immediately began thinking of an effective way to integrate sacred medicine experiences—especially because I planned to have many more of them.

Not long after, I serendipitously met ceremonial medicine practitioner, Jonathan, at another ceremony. I was drawn to his mother and felt called to introduce myself. His mother, Pilar, and I became immediate confidants and she quickly introduced me to her son, who happens to have the same name as my son and is around the same age as my son. I was overcome with emotion at the timing and synchronicity of our meeting and asked Pilar if she thought Jonathan would give me a hug. She spoke to him in Spanish and he quickly came over for an embrace. As he hugged me, he whispered the following phrase repeatedly in my ear, "Heal yourself to heal your son."

In that moment, Jonathan and his family became family to me. Shortly thereafter, Mayra and I continued our medicine journeys with Jonathan and his medicine partner Eden by his side.

The smaller ceremonies we experienced with Eden and Jonathan were powerful, yet I still struggled with the transition back to daily life, and felt like the overall experience was lacking tools to help me integrate the sacred ceremony. I was fortunate to have Mayra, a fellow coach and plant medicine mentor, to help me with questions, memories, and insights that came through after the ceremony ended. And while Jonathan and Eden are super helpful as ceremonial plant medicine practitioners, their focus is rightfully dedicated to ceremonial experiences.

Collectively, we wanted to find a way to support individuals through their integration process to truly maximize the benefits of the sacred medicine experiences. Personally, I'd been through so much searching, I needed to find a place to acknowledge and address the work I'd completed through ceremonial medicine. I didn't even realize the ramifications of searching in the name of finding something beyond myself until I saw this quote from my friend Wilderness Dawn Cowan on the importance of integration. She said, "If you avoid integration, you may be perpetually seeking knowledge in an attempt to control or find safety—when the safety is actually here; right now, with you."

Creating safety within is the precise reason the Companion Journal Supporting Sacred Medicine Experiences was conceived. Because God knows, seeking safety outside one's self is exhausting and futile. And yet, as individuals create safety within, through ceremonial medicine and other experiences, they can better connect with and share their gifts with the world. This team put forth great care and attention to assist individuals in finding affordable and accessible tools for integration practices in the name of creating a better world.

Like the man at my first ceremony claimed, we believe that becoming better and more healed as individuals is better for everyone. Individually and collectively, we've each experienced healing that extends far beyond our circumstances, even serving our lineage and paving a new path for future generations. Stay tuned for a book of stories detailing the wonderful and miraculous results from sacred medicine experiences and integration. In the meantime, we're so grateful you've picked up this integration journal and now have a place to integrate and record your sacred medicine journeys.

"There is a powerful driving force inside every human being that, once unleashed, can make any vision, dream, or desire a reality."

— Tony Robbins

Journaling and Strategic Visioning

Welcome to your sacred medicine journey! We're sharing this journal to help you gain the most from this experience to support your medicine experience and facilitate your integration process. The journal questions were created from a Neuro-Linguistic Programming (NLP) perspective. NLP uses a series of processes designed to align the mind (neuro), language (linguistic), and actions (programming). Strategic Visioning is an NLP process that uses visualization and commands to drop the elements of one's vision into their nervous system. Through strategic visioning, it's as if the desired result is guaranteed. In essence, after the process, the vision already occurred in the body and mind. This does two things, 1) Increases one's belief in a positive outcome, and 2) creates the space to allow full surrender and an expectation that the desired manifestation will arrive in the perfect time. Essentially, these tools help to generate personal alignment and support better performance.

Sacred medicines can create and expand one's alignment, vision, performance, and manifestation results. We believe combining these two powerful methods can produce greater outcomes. That's why we recommend strategic visioning in advance of the ceremony combined with journaling for integration.

The journaling questions will help support your process before, during, and after the ceremony. The questions were developed based on our experience with NLP and our intent to facilitate individual integration processes. In addition to being a potent healing tool, writing supports integration in the following ways:

1. The journal prompts you to recall the experience and gather the learnings so you can both recall them and use them in your daily life.
2. Detailing the experience and the learnings serves as documentation to revisit and expand your healing.

While some of the questions may seem repetitive, it's important to dedicate time to answering each one as the questions extract different responses that build on the prior learnings. As the insights are detailed, they also culminate to distill specific and actionable responses as the questions are answered.

This journal includes space to document 11 ceremonial medicine experiences. A single-use journal can be downloaded for free at bit.ly/IntegrationDownload.

"Drugs are about dulling perception, about addiction, and about behavioral repetition. What psychedelics are about is pattern dissolving experiences of an extraordinarily high or different awareness. They are the opposite of drugs. They promote questioning, they promote consciousness, they promote value examinations, they promote the reconstruction of behavioral patterns."

— Terrence Mckenna

Presuppositions for The Medicine Journey

The medicine journey occurs in the following segments:

- The Call to Medicine
- Ceremony Preparation
- Ceremony Experience
- Active Integration
- Aftercare and Routine Integration
- Sacred Medicine Community

Each stage of the journey is unique and important to the overall integration process. Presuppositions are a way to set the stage and declare expectations. This document will contain presuppositions and integration exercises for each segment of the sacred medicine journey. Following are observations we've made about working with sacred medicines. Acknowledging, understanding, and adhering to the suggested presuppositions will set the stage for a more positive overall experience and integration of sacred medicine.

The Call to Medicine

When you're ready to heal and awaken to the power within, you'll get the call to sacred plant medicine. The call is an opening to something greater. It's a whisper that reminds you there's something more and an invitation to explore what's behind the veil. It's a yearning to understand who you are, why you're here, and how to pursue your path. It's a deep recollection of unity and a summoning to return to your roots.

The connection to medicine arrives in synchronistic ways that are equally unquestionable and miraculous.

If you've been called to do this work, you've been chosen by your ancestors. You may not understand it, you will be challenged by it, but there's no question you'll heed the call. We're here to support your integration process.

The Call to Medicine Presuppositions

- I respect the medicine as a teacher.
- I honor the plants, animals, and tribes who make the sacred medicine available.
- Ceremonial medicine addresses the root causes of physical, spiritual, mental, and emotional limitations in order to bring greater ease to my life.

- Medicine is a vehicle to become more intimate with my highest self.
- Medicine is used to remove unwanted excess (thoughts, trauma, patterns, dis-ease) and increase wholeness.
- The body is the mind.
- There is no failure, only feedback.

Ceremony Preparation

When participating in a ceremony, the moment one sets the intentions to attend a ceremony, is when the work truly begins. Days upon arriving at the space, one begins to clear the mind in preparation to receive and do the work. Doing the work is a phrase to remind us that the medicine only introduces us to the purpose and work. Within our own self, we will work with the medicine to receive what we are in search of. Having an open heart and mind and powerful intentions are key to having an awakening through medicine.

In addition to mental preparation for ceremonies, there are a few physical guidelines to ensure effective and safe practices. Following are common ceremonial prerequisites.

- Fasting for at least six hours before the ceremony (some medicines may require longer fasting periods).
- Refraining from stimulants like energy drinks, coffee, hard synthetic drugs, and other harmful substances.
- Abstain from sexual intercourse and drinking alcohol for one to three days before and after the ceremony.

- Provide the Shaman or medicine practitioner notice of any prescription medications and/or physical or mental impairments.

- Eat as clean as possible and hydrate well on the days leading up to the ceremony (some medicines also require a dieta in which the Shaman will provide you a list of food to avoid or consume for the medicine as certain foods can affect the medicine).

- Prepare any particular items to bring to aid during the medicine journey.

- It's important not to bring active issues or problems into the ceremonial space. You can release this by dissolving cords and attachments with others, stating, "I forgive, I let go, and I move on."

Preparing and participating in a ceremony requires the physical, mental, energetic, and spiritual ability to look within and acknowledge the transformational process presented. This is true whether one is attending their first ceremony or their 100th ceremony. It is important to note that taking sacred medicines in environments with dissociative frequencies such as alcoholic/hard drugs, subliminal settings, and other casual settings for non-medicinal purposes is to play with fire and a sign of disrespect for the medicine and its healing purposes. This references back to the importance of intention setting and the true purpose of attending a ceremony.

Whether facilitating or participating within sacred medicines, set, setting, and participation all share significant importance. Setting begins with the placing of an altar. The altar is your connection to the Source and a witness of your own faith and experiences in it. As such, an altar is an energetic focal point to draw spiritual strength and is guided by the spirits of the medicine, ancestors, spirits of the realm, and consecrated artifacts. It serves as a beacon of communion with the energies of the ceremony or space. Each altar is unique, and its significance rests in the intention put into each item placed upon. Typically, we first lay down a cloth to separate the ceremonial items from the rest of the world. On top, we have medicinal items and artifacts. These include items such as tepis, kurpis (used for rapé), shamanic statues, collected bird feathers, essential oils, blessed plant sprays, aromatic smudging essentials such wild foraged plants (sage, rosemary, lavender, rose) copal, incense, and the medicine.

A variety of musical instruments often accompany the altar. The most important item on the altar is the medicine itself. When arranging an altar, harmony is what is of most importance. You should be able to bear witness to life and the Universe itself in your altar. Representations of the earth, sun, moon, death, and rebirth as well as the seasons and their elemental representations, are important aspects that demonstrate the power of the Universe.

When partaking in a ceremony, the setting has a big role in the process. The ceremony must be led by a Shaman or experienced and skilled practitioner residing within the space of a sacred and safe environment. It is best to have a ceremony in nature that is secluded outdoors and is one within a Pachamama setting. Pachamama is a term that refers to the great mother spirit of the earth. To embark on a therapeutic practice and ceremony, skilled facilitators and tribe members may also choose to have space holders or assistants. These space holders are appointed someone trusted and trained with the amount of responsibility to serve and participate in the ceremony.

When opening a space for ceremonial work, first, we must cleanse it and bless the space. Usually, sage or some form of smudging is used to approach the perimeter of the space and ask permission from the land and the spirits that reside to allow work within the space. The sage or smudging acts as a blessing while also cleaning the energies that have dwelled there. Smudging is the first opening to the ceremony. Once the area permits and all individuals are saged, then the ceremony begins.

Ceremony Preparation Presuppositions

- Sacred medicine experiences are unique to each person and each ceremony.
- Whatever the medicine says is appropriate for me, is what I will be shown and what I will take to heart.
- The subconscious mind contains many stories and the medicine may reveal them. Let it be for the purpose of understanding and healing.

During Ceremony, before Medicine

You showed up! Showing up is often the hardest part of ceremonial medicine. Now that you're here, allow your leaders to set the stage for your sacred medicine journey and begin the healing. Create an effective space to protect individual energies of those in the ceremony. Imagine creating an orb surrounding you with light to both keep your own energy contained and reflect the energy of others back to them.

Ceremony Presuppositions

- The medicine knows best.
- I come with an open heart and mind to the learning and the feedback offered by the medicine.
- Grounding and internal work allows clarity and stillness to come in and reveal the vision.

- I am open and flexible to the lessons the medicine teaches and the blessings it brings—even when they don't look like blessings.

- Individual energy should be contained and protected.

- I am in charge of my experience and the results.

- I have everything I need within. The medicine can help connect me to it—often by creating awareness of blockages and veils preventing connection and inviting me to remove them.

- Set, setting, and safety is extremely important in having a positive experience.

- The ceremony is only the beginning of work with sacred medicine. I am committed to continuing the work of becoming the next version of me.

- I surrender to the process and trust the medicine to do the work alongside me.

Active Integration

The sacred medicine offers insights, but the changes, results, and new manifestations occur because of the action taken on the insights given from the medicine. The journal questions will help draw out and distill the insights so you can truly integrate the learnings and put them into practice.

Active Integration Presuppositions

- There is no positive or negative to any experience with the medicine.
- I will take the time to integrate what I learn from each ceremony before coming back for a new ceremonial experience.

"Plant spirit medicine is the Shaman's way with plants. It recognizes that plants have spirit and that spirit is the strongest medicine. Spirit can heal the deepest reaches of the heart and soul."

— Eliot Cowan

Common Ceremonial Medicines

While sacred medicines are commonly used in various cultures across the world, it is not recommended to self-medicate or embark on a medicine journey without the support of a trained and experienced ceremonial medicine practitioner. An experienced practitioner can make sacred medicine recommendations for your personal situation and determine if you are fit for participation in ceremony.

Details provided below are based on ancestral, teachings, personal experience, and user reported claims. While aligned with current and trending research, the information provided is for educational purposes only. Details provided are not scientific, nor to be considered medical advice or recommendations.

"For traditional Amazonian tribespeople, Sananga is a powerful eye medicine used to sharpen night vision. For modern seekers of spiritual healing, however, Sananga does more than help with hunting."

— Psychedelic Times

Sananga

Increasing Inner and Outer Vision

Brief Overview:

This medicine teaches a great lesson related to endurance and discomfort. It teaches one to find comfort and solace in discomfort, leaving the individual in a state of tranquility and peace.

History:

Sananga eyedrops are traditionally used by tribesmen to embark on night hunts and amplify night vision.

Source:

This medicine comes from a shrub known as Tabernaemontana undulate. The medicinal properties are extracted from the shrub and made into a liquid that is applied to the eyes.

Beneficial Usage:

Sananga can be an aid to move through difficult, emotional uprisings. When working with this medicine regularly, life's uprisings and its discomforts lessen.

Common Conditions Addressed:

Sananga is known to treat inner and outer vision, including glaucoma, cataracts, headaches, migraines, near and far sightedness, astigmatism, and other ocular ailments. It's also helpful for treating migraines and helps to connect one to intuition and inner psyche to connect with inner vision and one's own power of manifestation. It is often used to further visionary states and continue to integrate them.

Precautions:

It is not recommended to use Sananga when wearing contact lens.

Delivery System:

These eyedrops are administered by simply dropping liquid into the eyes. An immediate stinging sensation dissipates within seconds to minutes depending on the strength of the extract.

Experience Overview:

The experience of Sananga is rather quick, but intense. As the medicine is dispelled, it leaves one in a tranquil state. Some, but not all, receive visions through use of the medicine.

Effects:

One will find the effects to vary depending on the severity of the eye conditions. When used at bedtime, it is common to wake up with mucus in the eyes known as rheum, or pink color in the eye due to the overnight cleansing effects of the medicine. Use of Sananga can help one connect to and intensify the dream realm and prior medicinal states.

Post Experience State:

Immediate relaxation and help with relaxation and tension release.

Suggested Regimen:

Sananga is typically added to as an opening to sacred medicine ceremony. One can also practice Sananga medicine daily. It is sometimes recommended to embark on a 30 day or more Sananga journey where Sananga is used once in the morning and once in the evening. This daily practice is used to help one step into their visionary path and increase connections to inner and outer vision.

"Physically it [the tobacco] cleans the intestines of parasites and negative energies, but because the intestines connect

to the brain, if the intestines get liberated,

the brain gets liberated as well."

— Amazonian traditional healer (curandero) and Maestro Tabaquero with 36 years of clinical experience[1]

[1] https://www.frontiersin.org/articles/10.3389/fphar.2020.594591/full

Rapé

Shamanic Snuff

Brief Overview:

Pronounced "ha-peh" or "rapay," this medicine is commonly referred to as Shamanic snuff and is made of ground up tobacco ashes known as Nicotiana Rustica. The tobacco ash is not the same as the common tobacco cigarettes which contain Nicotiana Tabacum. Rapé is primarily used prior to and in preparation for ceremony and throughout the duration of a ceremony.

History:

This medicine is ground for three days and three nights while invoking powerful intentions and prayers.

Source:

Rapé is sourced from Brazil, Peru, Bolivia and other Amazonian regions.

Beneficial Usage:

Rapé medicine is used for a physical, energetic, and emotional level reset. On the physical level, the ash attaches to all mucus membranes and helps clear airways. Some say after they experience Rapé for the first time, it is as if they can truly breathe for the first time. On an energetic level, Rapé aids in removing blockages, negative vibrations, and helps with grounding. Finally, on the emotional level, it helps to reset emotions and connects one to their higher self. Rapé is a useful medicine that can be used on a daily basis for integration.

Common Conditions Addressed:

Rapé is used to ground one's self before, throughout, and after a ceremony. It can also be used as a mucus defensive, headache resolver, and alignment tool for daily medication practices.

Precautions:

Rapé is not recommended for women who are pregnant.

Delivery System:

Despite being referred to as snuff, Rapé is not snorted nor inhaled. It's administered directly and blown through the nose with a tool called a Kuripe for self-administration and a Tepi when administered by another.

Experience Overview:

The power of Rapé is placed in the palm of the hand. It is then scooped into the applicator while setting intentions. The left nostril represents release and death of old energy while the right nostril is to welcome new intentions and new energies. To start, the Rapé is blown first through the left nostril to balance the female to male energy duality. After a breath and centering, the medicine is blown through the right nostril for greater balance. After presented in both nostrils, one sits with the medicine only breathing through their mouth. When they are ready, they blow their nose to release the remnants.

Effects:

When one is sitting with Rapé, they can feel bodily and energetic sensations. They are instantly grounded and in their body, while the heart is open. Often, tears flow naturally. One may experience lightheadedness, dizziness, ringing in the ears, and general connection to the nerves and body, sometimes with excessive mucus or spit.

Post Experience State:

Feeling a shift of energy, either up or down, as well as increased grounding and release.

Suggested Regimen:

Rapé can be used daily as an alignment mechanism, or for ceremonial purposes only.

"Kambo medicine dissolves veils or blocks

you have around the heart."

— Rebecca Naylor

Kambo

The Vaccine of the Jungle

Brief Overview:

This medicine is used by Indigenous tribes in the Amazon Rainforest to heal, cleanse, and strengthen the mind, body, and spirit. It is one of the most powerful antibiotics and anti-inflammatories in the world.

History:

The medicinal properties of Kambo were discovered when an Ayahuasca Shaman's entire village was becoming ill and dying. The Shaman tried everything he knew in his power to heal the village members. Because nothing was working, he prayed to mother Ayahuasca and went on his journey. In his visions, he was led to a tree. Upon standing there, frogs began to fall in front of him and all around him. It was the Kambo frog that came to him in the vision. By using the frog's natural medicine, the Shaman was able to save his entire village. Before hunting, tribesmen would partake in Kambo to aid in capturing and manifesting their prey. Today's medicine users also use Kambo as a tool to manifest greater health, mental clarity, and to achieve their dreams.

Source:

The medicine is derived from the waxy poisonous secretion of the giant monkey tree frog, Phyllomedusa bicolor. The wax is made of many peptides that are beneficial to the body and the brain.

Beneficial Usage:

Kambo is used to detox the body and organs to improve mental functioning and reset cellular memory. This medicine has many benefits, such as building strength and immunity while addressing physical and mental illnesses. In addition, it also aids in removing negative and "bad" energies or curses, impacting one's emotional, spiritual, mental, or physical health.

Common Conditions Addressed:

Kambo cleanses and strengthens the immune system and destroys pathogenic microorganisms, relieves joint pain, and can address conditions like Alzheimer's, Parkinson's, mental disorders, organ issues, AIDS, and herpes—just to name a few.

Precautions:

Kambo should not be practiced by those who have heart problems, blood pressure issues, are prone to seizures, have experienced brain tumors or deficiencies, and terminal illnesses.

Delivery System:

Kambo is applied to small burns on the skin and quickly enters the lymphatic system enticing a purge and waking up the body's ability to heal itself.

Experience Overview:

Kambo allows one to feel the body's intoxications by the venom, feel depths of great discomfort, and release the bio-plasticity of deep stomach and gut bacteria, bile, and energy. Through the process, individuals can see for oneself the releasing and shedding of external and internal layers through purging. This leaves one in a state of awe of witnessing the body's transformation through release.

Effects:

Kambo will give an overwhelming sensation of cold like symptoms, and out of body discomforts. It's a physical experience, not a psychoactive one. Depending on the dose, one may feel as if their entire body is shutting down. During the session, one enters into a deep commune with the spirit of Kambo where prayer is the most effective form of processing the medicine.

Post Experience State:

Individuals may experience throat soreness, being tired, or even being full of energy. The face may reflect swelling and the body may experience feelings of being "lighter" energetically.

Suggested Regimen:

Depending on the intention behind sitting with medicine, frequency and usage varies. Kambo is best experienced three times in a lunar cycle. For someone looking to do emotional work, 2-3 times in a lunar cycle is recommended, for those dealing with deep physical ailments, up to monthly ceremonies are sometimes suggested.

"...psilocybin can offer a means to reconnect to our true nature—our authentic self—and thereby help find meaning in our lives."

— Mary Cosimano

Psilocybin Mushrooms

The Medicine of the Mind

Brief Overview:

Psilocybin mushrooms contain psilocybin and have the ability to produce powerful healing through feelings, visions, and physical experiencing. With over 100+ species of mushrooms, these fungi can be used to heal a variety of ailments, disorders, physical issues, and more.

History:

Mushrooms have been around from the beginning of time. In modern days, Maria Sabina, a medicine woman in the 1950s, from Oaxaca, Mexico used psilocybin mushrooms for healing and religious ceremonies. In the late 1950s, she personally introduced medicine to the first white man, exposing psilocybin to the west with an article from Time Magazine, entitled “Seeking the Magic Mushroom.”

Source:

With 100+ species of mushrooms, there are more species of psilocybin mushrooms than marijuana strains. They grow worldwide and can be crossbred to produce different experiences.

Beneficial Usage:

From underground psychedelic clinics to the research being done at John Hopkins, it is now more and more plausible for an average person to seek psilocybin therapy. As of December 2021, psilocybin has been decriminalized in several cities and states across the United States.

Multiple locations are serving mushrooms in therapeutic facilities and ongoing research is underway to support medicinal use of mushrooms in the modern-day psychedelic renaissance.

Each journey is unique to every individual and will vary based on dosage. Mushrooms can be ingested in large ceremonial settings for intensive healing or in microdose forms for slow, longitudinal healings.

Common Conditions Addressed:

Mushrooms have had breakthrough treatment data collected for anxiety and depression. According to a 2021 article published on WebMD.com, "The psychedelic drug psilocybin – found in 'magic mushrooms' performed just as well as a widely used antidepressant in easing the symptoms of major depression, and outperformed the common prescription medication on a range of secondary measures, results of a small-scale phase II study show."[2]

Precautions:

Mushrooms should not be ingested by those who have undiagnosed mental illness, as they can trigger psychotic breaks. In addition, mushrooms should not be used as escapism.

Delivery System:

Psilocybin can be ingested in many different ways. It can be brewed

[2] https://www.webmd.com/depression/news/20210415/study-magic-mushrooms-may-best-drug-for-depression

into tea, taken in capsule form, combined with other substances, or eaten as is—the possibilities are endless.

Experience Overview:

Depending on the form of ingestion, one may feel the spirit of mushrooms immediately or within 45 minutes. The effects can last around four or more hours. Each and every experience of mushrooms is different and varies. No experience is ever the same.

Effects:

Psilocybin can create profound visionary states. Connecting with the inner and outer vision, a mushroom journey can also connect one closely to their intuition. During the experience, mushrooms can cause one to purge energetically or physically. Users frequently report an overall feeling of oneness and connection to Source energy while under the influence of psylocibin.

Post Experience State:

Feelings of energy and motivation, or sometimes in need of rest. In some cases, introspection.

Suggested Regimen:

Microdosing is recommended to begin one's exploration to psilocybin. Full doses of mushrooms are recommended for those looking for deep healing and connecting with their consciousness in and outside of themselves.

"In 20 minutes, you're going to get two thousand years of experience in your face."

— Mike Tyson

Bufo, 5-MeO-DMT (Bufo Alvarius)

El Sapito (little toad)—The God Molecule

Brief Overview:

The Bufo Alvarius toad holds the deepest of properties in regards to transformation and rebirth. When the substance of the toad's venom is vaporized and inhaled, one will travel directly to Source. Its visions and impact can only be described as peak ayahuasca experiences. This medicine has radically changed countless individual by enabling them to connect with infinite intelligence and become open to healing within.

History:

The Indigenous history of Bufo is very sacred and guarded. Most Bufo tribes deny contact with the outer world.

Source:

Bufo is known commonly to the areas of Sonora, Mexico and parts of Arizona. This dessert toad holds a venom that, when extracted from its gland and dried, becomes 5-MeO-DMT. This molecule is 10x stronger than other traditional plant formations of N, N-dimethyltryptamine (DMT).

Beneficial Usage:

One's own intentions within the context of personal and interpersonal healing can be directly worked with and obtained through the spirit of Bufo.

Common Conditions Addressed:

For people struggling with mental illness, addictions, habitual patterns, and lack of spiritual consciousness—working with Bufo is revolutionary. For anyone wanting to further their connections to Source and spirit or to ask the Universe questions, this molecule holds many answers and insights.

Precautions:

Bufo should not be practiced by those who are taking prescribed mood stabilizer medications/SSRI's/MAOI's, etc.

Delivery System:

Bufo is vaporized and inhaled. The journey lasts about 20 minutes.

Experience Overview:

The entire process only lasts for about 20 minutes before the effects wear off. However, the impression of the medicine and its teachings can stay with the individual for many moons and lifetimes—depending on the depth of their integration process.

Effects:

Bufo is indescribable. Its effects come on within seconds and are unique to each individual. Some report seeing the light, being the light, and experiencing a deep state of comfort. Others encounter bodily sensations and receive profound insights related to their experience in this lifetime and others.

Post Experience State:

An understanding of higher realms of consciousness and having a direct connection to it. Integration and visitations at night during sleep between the hours of 2-4 a.m.

Suggested Regimen:

Some people only need Bufo once in their life and they are fully fulfilled with all questions answered. Others receive a calling to work further within the medicine. Bufo itself provides the suggested regimen.

Depending on the potency of the medicine,
Huachuma can produce visions and dream-like states.
It is during these experiences that many users have
received valuable lessons, guidance, clarity,
breakthroughs, healing, and awareness of their divinity.
People attending ceremonies have reported meeting their
spirit guides, ancestors, and otherworldly beings who
helped them in some way. Many users will experience
bliss-like states, heightened senses, waves of emotions,
and a sense of being connected with all life."

— Zahrah Sita

Huachuma (San Pedro Cactus)

The Grandfather Spirit

Brief Overview:

Huachuma is known as echinopsis pachanoi, trichocereus bridgesii, or San Pedro cactus. The grandfather spirit serves as the heart of the Universe. This cactus contains mescaline and is indefinitely life-changing by promoting introspection, healing, and the opening of the heart. Experiencing this medicine is a very long journey that comes with intense energy but can also be very gentle, just like a grandfather.

History:

The cactus has been used by Indigenously since the beginning of time from our ancestors and Ancient America as religious sacraments.

Source:

San Pedro Cactus is native to Peru and Bolivia.

Beneficial Usage:

San Pedro Cactus opens one's heart to connect with feeling and energy. With this linkage, one can enter a process to heal themselves physically, spiritually, emotionally, and mentally.

Common Conditions Addressed:

The grandfather medicine helps with spiritual connections but also can aide in expanding creativity, connecting with the heart, balancing emotions, and increasing feelings of love. It also addresses trauma, depression, Post Traumatic Stress Disorder (PTSD), other mental health disorders, and addictions. It also aides in tackling chronic ailments, and physical symptoms such as infertility, low and high blood pressure, diabetes, hypertension, anxiety, and more.

Precautions:

One should not ingest San Pedro Cactus in an ungrounded state of mind. It may also not be recommended for those with severe physical health conditions such as Chron's disease, kidney failure/issues, intestinal issues, and other serious diseases.

Delivery System:

This cactus can be taken in brew form or ingested as a powder in a tea or as a liquid substance.

Experience Overview:

Once this medicine is ingested, one may not notice the effects until they are deep in the process. The entire journey can last for 12 or more hours. At times, this medicine can be visual, and one can experience dream-like states. This medicine teaches lessons and instills wisdom.

Effects:

One can enter into a deep state of physical connections, visual journeys, and internal downloads from Source. The journey may feel a bit like dream like state. Deeply grounded in the medicine, one may also feel the love and heart opening effects of the Universe.

Post Experience State:

Being tired and in need of rest or full of energy. Full of love, compassion, and gratitude. Awareness of connection to the body in places that need attention.

Suggested Regimen:

To be determined under the guidance of a skilled practitioner or shamanic guide in a ceremonial setting.

"In its proper ceremonial setting, under compassionate and experienced guidance, the plant – or, as tradition has it, the spirit of the plant – puts people in touch with their repressed pain and trauma, the very factors that drive all dysfunctional mind states. Consciously experiencing our primal pain loosens its hold on us. Thus ayahuasca may achieve in a few sittings what many years of psychotherapy can only aspire to do. People can re-experience long-lost inner qualities such as wholeness, trust, love and a sense of possibility. They quite literally remember themselves."

— Gabor Maté

Yagé/Ayahuasca

A Vehicle for Spiritual Enlightenment

Brief Overview:

Typically, Yagé is served by a Taita—a Yagé shaman, which is a Quechua word that means "father," "guide," or "spiritual leader." In order to serve Yagé, one must undergo an intense apprenticeship of several years while passing a series of tests under the wings of an elder or the Taita. DMT, which is the active compound found in this brew, exists in all living things and is derived directly from the earth.

History:

Yagé is a version of ayahuasca sacred to Columbian tribes. It has been served in multiple forms for 500+ years.

Source:

Yagé is known as ayahuasca from Colombia. It is made from banisteriopsis caapi and other plant admixtures. There are different types of Yagé and most are served in a brew format.

Beneficial Usage:

Work with Yagé can be an intense form of therapy where the answers are given without questions. One must simply ask and be ready to receive.

Common Conditions Addressed:

Yagé addresses spiritual sickness, physical illnesses, and unresolved traumas. It often seeks those looking for enlightenment and to surpass energetic and physical blockages preventing them from living their most fulfilled life.

Precautions:

Yagé cannot be taken by women on their moon cycle, anyone on antidepressants and/or antianxiety medications, or those with high blood pressure or any heart conditions.

Delivery System:

Taitas prepare the brew as a mixture of sacred Yagé vine cuts of chagropanga and chacruna.

Experience Overview:

One ingests the brewed medicine and its effects comes in waves throughout the session. Typically, ceremonies are held at night, but there are exceptions for day ceremonies. The journey can be long journey and can initiate an activation of bodily functions, emotional connections, and mostly visual and mental expressions. It is something that one has to testify in regards to the connection and presence of mother earth and all living things within this medicine.

Effects:

Yagé is a very cosmic and individualized experience. The spirit of ayahuasca displays visons in forms only comprehensible to the individual experiencing the medicine. Physically, it can cause one to purge and allow one to physically feel cellular awareness.

Post Experience State:

Filled with energy and experiencing vivid dreams with powerful messages and manifesting prowess. Having a primal desire to commune with nature and ability to feel, see, and hear the vibration of natural elements. Feelings of alignment, desire, and manifestation ease. Lack of unconscious behavior.

Suggested Regimen:

In order to sit with Yagé, one must go under evaluation by the Taita, who will determine if fit to sit with the medicine and the applicable dose(s) and frequency.

"The modern person is drawn to the shamanic archetype—the vision of sacred earth, revelatory word, and multidimensional cosmos—finds himself horrified by contemporary society and the accelerating processes of global destruction it has unleashed."

— Daniel Pinchbeck

Cultural Reminder

These mystical altered state experiences continue to travel through the evolution of time. Yet the people—the essence of these sacred medicines and practices—continue to remind us that we're here to respect these ancient ways of life. When using these medicines, it's essential to come from a place of respect, service, and acknowledgment of the Indigenous communities who cultivated and kept these ancient ways alive. In addition to respecting the communities, it's critical to KEEP these cultures, traditions, tribes, and lineages alive. As sacred medicine practices become more mainstream, popular, and publicized, the effects of industrialization compound the reasons why it's important to give back and advocate for the tribes. It's important to ensure medicines are ethically sourced and supported in order to preserve the jungle and its inhabitants so they can continue healing the world through natural means.

Using these practices and substances comes with great responsibility. Miriam Volat, ecologist and cofounder of the small family foundation Riverstyx, reiterates this, noting, "If you're going to respect these medicines, then you have to be respectful of the human cultures that have maintained a relationship with these medicines for so many years."

"Life lived in the absence of the psychedelic experience that primordial shamanism is based on is life trivialized, life denied, life enslaved to the ego."

— Terence McKenna

Ceremonial Medicine Experience #1

Ceremony Preparation

Scheduled Ceremony Date, Practitioner, Location, Setting, Notes

What are you committed to and honoring through this medicine work?

What did you come to experience?

What do you believe about your healing and your experience with this medicine?

Pure intent means you believe it. What do you intend to shift through this work?

What constructed limitations would you like to address through the medicine? A constructed limitation is like a limiting belief. It's something you believe that is not actually true. For example, believing "I'm not good enough" is limited. In actuality, every single person is made of the same magic with the same potential as another. Therefore, this belief is constructed.

What do you want to grow?

What do you want to curtail?

What will you say when you achieve the healing you desire right now?

During Ceremony, before Medicine

What's the healing you came for?

What are you ready for?

Speak to your higher self, your best friend, your soul. The energy is ready to support you. Help is available because you ask. What will you ask for?

Active Integration through Initial Insights

What visions, feelings, and/or emotional purging occurred during the ceremony and how did it present for you after the ceremony?

Were there parts of the ceremony that were challenging or painful?

What did you learn?

What structures in your life do you want to dissolve as a result of what you experienced?

How will you act on what you learned? Drop information into your heart and hands, and incorporate it into your practical work.

What do you believe as your pure intent now?

Did your belief or intention change?

If there is a change in your belief and/or intention, why do you think that is?

What's next?

Aftercare and Routine Integration

What remembrances or epiphanies came up for you in the week following your ceremony?

Did you experience any physical symptoms or changes in your physical experience?

What are your intentions to continue your healing work?

What commitments do you make to yourself to support your integration over the next 31 days and beyond?

Routine Day 1 Notes

Routine Day 2 Notes

Routine Day 3 Notes

Routine Day 4 Notes

Routine Day 5 Notes

Routine Day 6 Notes

Routine Day 7 Notes

Routine Day 8 Notes

Routine Day 9 Notes

Routine Day 10 Notes

Routine Day 11 Notes

Routine Day 12 Notes

Routine Day 13 Notes

Routine Day 14 Notes

Routine Day 15 Notes

Routine Day 16 Notes

Routine Day 17 Notes

Routine Day 18 Notes

Routine Day 19 Notes

Routine Day 20 Notes

Routine Day 21 Notes

Routine Day 22 Notes

Routine Day 23 Notes

Routine Day 24 Notes

Routine Day 25 Notes

Routine Day 26 Notes

Routine Day 27 Notes

Routine Day 28 Notes

Routine Day 29 Notes

Routine Day 30 Notes

Routine Day 31 Notes

How do you feel about your commitment to the daily actions to support your integration after the ceremony?

Sacred Medicine Community Healing

What is the most valuable experience I can offer to the sacred medicine community?

How can individuals in a sacred medicine community best support me?

Note Pages

Coloring Page

Sketch Page

"When we do plant medicine, and we see love, we realize right then and there that it was never apart from us, that in fact it was a part of us."

— Gerard Armond Powell

Ceremonial Medicine Experience #2

Ceremony Preparation

Scheduled Ceremony Date, Practitioner, Location, Setting, Notes

What are you committed to and honoring through this medicine work?

What did you come to experience?

What do you believe about your healing and your experience with this medicine?

Pure intent means you believe it. What do you intend to shift through this work?

What constructed limitations would you like to address through the medicine? A constructed limitation is like a limiting belief. It's something you believe that is not actually true. For example, believing "I'm not good enough" is limited. In actuality, every single person is made of the same magic with the same potential as another. Therefore, this belief is constructed.

What do you want to grow?

What do you want to curtail?

What will you say when you achieve the healing you desire right now?

During Ceremony, before Medicine

What's the healing you came for?

What are you ready for?

Speak to your higher self, your best friend, your soul. The energy is ready to support you. Help is available because you ask. What will you ask for?

Active Integration through Initial Insights

What visions, feelings, and/or emotional purging occurred during the ceremony and how did it present for you after the ceremony?

Were there parts of the ceremony that were challenging or painful?

What did you learn?

What structures in your life do you want to dissolve as a result of what you experienced?

How will you act on what you learned? Drop information into your heart and hands, and incorporate it into your practical work.

What do you believe as your pure intent now?

Did your belief or intention change?

If there is a change in your belief and/or intention, why do you think that is?

What's next?

Aftercare and Routine Integration

What remembrances or epiphanies came up for you in the week following your ceremony?

Did you experience any physical symptoms or changes in your physical experience?

What are your intentions to continue your healing work?

What commitments do you make to yourself to support your integration over the next 31 days and beyond?

Routine Day 1 Notes

Routine Day 2 Notes

Routine Day 3 Notes

Routine Day 4 Notes

Routine Day 5 Notes

Routine Day 6 Notes

Routine Day 7 Notes

Routine Day 8 Notes

Routine Day 9 Notes

....

....

....

Routine Day 10 Notes

....

....

....

Routine Day 11 Notes

....

....

....

Routine Day 12 Notes

....

....

....

Routine Day 13 Notes

....

....

....

Routine Day 14 Notes

Routine Day 15 Notes

Routine Day 16 Notes

Routine Day 17 Notes

Routine Day 18 Notes

Routine Day 19 Notes

Routine Day 20 Notes

Routine Day 21 Notes

Routine Day 22 Notes

Routine Day 23 Notes

Routine Day 24 Notes

Routine Day 25 Notes

Routine Day 26 Notes

Routine Day 27 Notes

Routine Day 28 Notes

Routine Day 29 Notes

Routine Day 30 Notes

Routine Day 31 Notes

How do you feel about your commitment to the daily actions to support your integration after the ceremony?

Sacred Medicine Community Healing

What is the most valuable experience I can offer to the sacred medicine community?

How can individuals in a sacred medicine community best support me?

Note Pages

Coloring Page

Sketch Page

"You give up knowing you know, to be it all."

— Ram Dass

Ceremonial Medicine Experience #3

Ceremony Preparation

Scheduled Ceremony Date, Practitioner, Location, Setting, Notes

What are you committed to and honoring through this medicine work?

What did you come to experience?

What do you believe about your healing and your experience with this medicine?

Pure intent means you believe it. What do you intend to shift through this work?

What constructed limitations would you like to address through the medicine? A constructed limitation is like a limiting belief. It's something you believe that is not actually true. For example, believing "I'm not good enough" is limited. In actuality, every single person is made of the same magic with the same potential as another. Therefore, this belief is constructed.

What do you want to grow?

What do you want to curtail?

What will you say when you achieve the healing you desire right now?

During Ceremony, before Medicine

What's the healing you came for?

What are you ready for?

Speak to your higher self, your best friend, your soul. The energy is ready to support you. Help is available because you ask. What will you ask for?

Active Integration through Initial Insights

What visions, feelings, and/or emotional purging occurred during the ceremony and how did it present for you after the ceremony?

Were there parts of the ceremony that were challenging or painful?

What did you learn?

What structures in your life do you want to dissolve as a result of what you experienced?

How will you act on what you learned? Drop information into your heart and hands, and incorporate it into your practical work.

What do you believe as your pure intent now?

Did your belief or intention change?

If there is a change in your belief and/or intention, why do you think that is?

What's next?

Aftercare and Routine Integration

What remembrances or epiphanies came up for you in the week following your ceremony?

Did you experience any physical symptoms or changes in your physical experience?

What are your intentions to continue your healing work?

What commitments do you make to yourself to support your integration over the next 31 days and beyond?

Routine Day 1 Notes

Routine Day 2 Notes

Routine Day 3 Notes

Routine Day 4 Notes

Routine Day 5 Notes

Routine Day 6 Notes

Routine Day 7 Notes

Routine Day 8 Notes

Routine Day 9 Notes

Routine Day 10 Notes

Routine Day 11 Notes

Routine Day 12 Notes

Routine Day 13 Notes

Routine Day 14 Notes

Routine Day 15 Notes

Routine Day 16 Notes

Routine Day 17 Notes

Routine Day 18 Notes

Routine Day 19 Notes

Routine Day 20 Notes

Routine Day 21 Notes

Routine Day 22 Notes

Routine Day 23 Notes

Routine Day 24 Notes

Routine Day 25 Notes

Routine Day 26 Notes

Routine Day 27 Notes

Routine Day 28 Notes

Routine Day 29 Notes

Routine Day 30 Notes

Routine Day 31 Notes

How do you feel about your commitment to the daily actions to support your integration after the ceremony?

Sacred Medicine Community Healing

What is the most valuable experience I can offer to the sacred medicine community?

How can individuals in a sacred medicine community best support me?

Note Pages

Coloring Page

Sketch Page

"Plant medicine can help people recover from addiction, heal heartbreak as well as awaken souls to their own powerful spiritual nature."

— Vishen Lakhiani

Ceremonial Medicine Experience #4

Ceremony Preparation

Scheduled Ceremony Date, Practitioner, Location, Setting, Notes

What are you committed to and honoring through this medicine work?

What did you come to experience?

What do you believe about your healing and your experience with this medicine?

Pure intent means you believe it. What do you intend to shift through this work?

What constructed limitations would you like to address through the medicine? A constructed limitation is like a limiting belief. It's something you believe that is not actually true. For example, believing "I'm not good enough" is limited. In actuality, every single person is made of the same magic with the same potential as another. Therefore, this belief is constructed.

What do you want to grow?

What do you want to curtail?

What will you say when you achieve the healing you desire right now?

During Ceremony, before Medicine

What's the healing you came for?

What are you ready for?

Speak to your higher self, your best friend, your soul. The energy is ready to support you. Help is available because you ask. What will you ask for?

Active Integration through Initial Insights

What visions, feelings, and/or emotional purging occurred during the ceremony and how did it present for you after the ceremony?

Were there parts of the ceremony that were challenging or painful?

What did you learn?

What structures in your life do you want to dissolve as a result of what you experienced?

How will you act on what you learned? Drop information into your heart and hands, and incorporate it into your practical work.

What do you believe as your pure intent now?

Did your belief or intention change?

If there is a change in your belief and/or intention, why do you think that is?

What's next?

Aftercare and Routine Integration

What remembrances or epiphanies came up for you in the week following your ceremony?

Did you experience any physical symptoms or changes in your physical experience?

What are your intentions to continue your healing work?

What commitments do you make to yourself to support your integration over the next 31 days and beyond?

Routine Day 1 Notes

Routine Day 2 Notes

Routine Day 3 Notes

Routine Day 4 Notes

Routine Day 5 Notes

Routine Day 6 Notes

Routine Day 7 Notes

Routine Day 8 Notes

Routine Day 9 Notes

Routine Day 10 Notes

Routine Day 11 Notes

Routine Day 12 Notes

Routine Day 13 Notes

Routine Day 14 Notes

Routine Day 15 Notes

Routine Day 16 Notes

Routine Day 17 Notes

Routine Day 18 Notes

Routine Day 19 Notes

Routine Day 20 Notes

Routine Day 21 Notes

Routine Day 22 Notes

Routine Day 23 Notes

Routine Day 24 Notes

Routine Day 25 Notes

Routine Day 26 Notes

Routine Day 27 Notes

Routine Day 28 Notes

Routine Day 29 Notes

Routine Day 30 Notes

Routine Day 31 Notes

How do you feel about your commitment to the daily actions to support your integration after the ceremony?

Sacred Medicine Community Healing

What is the most valuable experience I can offer to the sacred medicine community?

How can individuals in a sacred medicine community best support me?

Note Pages

Coloring Page

Sketch Page

"Because I can swim in the immense.

Because I can swim in all forms."

— Maria Sabina

Ceremonial Medicine Experience #5

Ceremony Preparation

Scheduled Ceremony Date, Practitioner, Location, Setting, Notes

What are you committed to and honoring through this medicine work?

What did you come to experience?

What do you believe about your healing and your experience with this medicine?

Pure intent means you believe it. What do you intend to shift through this work?

What constructed limitations would you like to address through the medicine? A constructed limitation is like a limiting belief. It's something you believe that is not actually true. For example, believing "I'm not good enough" is limited. In actuality, every single person is made of the same magic with the same potential as another. Therefore, this belief is constructed.

What do you want to grow?

What do you want to curtail?

What will you say when you achieve the healing you desire right now?

During Ceremony, before Medicine

What's the healing you came for?

What are you ready for?

Speak to your higher self, your best friend, your soul. The energy is ready to support you. Help is available because you ask. What will you ask for?

Active Integration through Initial Insights

What visions, feelings, and/or emotional purging occurred during the ceremony and how did it present for you after the ceremony?

Were there parts of the ceremony that were challenging or painful?

What did you learn?

What structures in your life do you want to dissolve as a result of what you experienced?

How will you act on what you learned? Drop information into your heart and hands, and incorporate it into your practical work.

What do you believe as your pure intent now?

Did your belief or intention change?

If there is a change in your belief and/or intention, why do you think that is?

What's next?

Aftercare and Routine Integration

What remembrances or epiphanies came up for you in the week following your ceremony?

Did you experience any physical symptoms or changes in your physical experience?

What are your intentions to continue your healing work?

What commitments do you make to yourself to support your integration over the next 31 days and beyond?

Routine Day 1 Notes

Routine Day 2 Notes

Routine Day 3 Notes

Routine Day 4 Notes

Routine Day 5 Notes

Routine Day 6 Notes

Routine Day 7 Notes

Routine Day 8 Notes

Routine Day 9 Notes

Routine Day 10 Notes

Routine Day 11 Notes

Routine Day 12 Notes

Routine Day 13 Notes

Routine Day 14 Notes

Routine Day 15 Notes

Routine Day 16 Notes

Routine Day 17 Notes

Routine Day 18 Notes

Routine Day 19 Notes

Routine Day 20 Notes

Routine Day 21 Notes

Routine Day 22 Notes

Routine Day 23 Notes

Routine Day 24 Notes

Routine Day 25 Notes

Routine Day 26 Notes

Routine Day 27 Notes

Routine Day 28 Notes

Routine Day 29 Notes

Routine Day 30 Notes

Routine Day 31 Notes

How do you feel about your commitment to the daily actions to support your integration after the ceremony?

Sacred Medicine Community Healing

What is the most valuable experience I can offer to the sacred medicine community?

How can individuals in a sacred medicine community best support me?

Note Pages

Coloring Page

Sketch Page

"Psychedelics open users to natural and supernatural visions and experiences that can help people who are dealing with addictions and terminal diseases. The influence of psychedelics can connect them to a larger world that transcends the five senses, enabling them to see their place in it."

— Ian Thomsen

Ceremonial Medicine Experience #6

Ceremony Preparation

Scheduled Ceremony Date, Practitioner, Location, Setting, Notes

What are you committed to and honoring through this medicine work?

What did you come to experience?

What do you believe about your healing and your experience with this medicine?

Pure intent means you believe it. What do you intend to shift through this work?

What constructed limitations would you like to address through the medicine? A constructed limitation is like a limiting belief. It's something you believe that is not actually true. For example, believing "I'm not good enough" is limited. In actuality, every single person is made of the same magic with the same potential as another. Therefore, this belief is constructed.

What do you want to grow?

What do you want to curtail?

What will you say when you achieve the healing you desire right now?

During Ceremony, before Medicine

What's the healing you came for?

What are you ready for?

Speak to your higher self, your best friend, your soul. The energy is ready to support you. Help is available because you ask. What will you ask for?

Active Integration through Initial Insights

What visions, feelings, and/or emotional purging occurred during the ceremony and how did it present for you after the ceremony?

Were there parts of the ceremony that were challenging or painful?

What did you learn?

What structures in your life do you want to dissolve as a result of what you experienced?

How will you act on what you learned? Drop information into your heart and hands, and incorporate it into your practical work.

What do you believe as your pure intent now?

Did your belief or intention change?

If there is a change in your belief and/or intention, why do you think that is?

What's next?

Aftercare and Routine Integration

What remembrances or epiphanies came up for you in the week following your ceremony?

Did you experience any physical symptoms or changes in your physical experience?

What are your intentions to continue your healing work?

What commitments do you make to yourself to support your integration over the next 31 days and beyond?

Routine Day 1 Notes

Routine Day 2 Notes

Routine Day 3 Notes

Routine Day 4 Notes

Routine Day 5 Notes

Routine Day 6 Notes

Routine Day 7 Notes

Routine Day 8 Notes

Routine Day 9 Notes

Routine Day 10 Notes

Routine Day 11 Notes

Routine Day 12 Notes

Routine Day 13 Notes

Routine Day 14 Notes

Routine Day 15 Notes

Routine Day 16 Notes

Routine Day 17 Notes

Routine Day 18 Notes

Routine Day 19 Notes

Routine Day 20 Notes

Routine Day 21 Notes

Routine Day 22 Notes

Routine Day 23 Notes

Routine Day 24 Notes

Routine Day 25 Notes

Routine Day 26 Notes

Routine Day 27 Notes

Routine Day 28 Notes

Routine Day 29 Notes

Routine Day 30 Notes

Routine Day 31 Notes

How do you feel about your commitment to the daily actions to support your integration after the ceremony?

Sacred Medicine Community Healing

What is the most valuable experience I can offer to the sacred medicine community?

How can individuals in a sacred medicine community best support me?

Note Pages

Coloring Page

Sketch Page

"The healing is about how you renegotiate reality based on the experiences you have."

— Charles Flores

Ceremonial Medicine Experience #7

Ceremony Preparation

Scheduled Ceremony Date, Practitioner, Location, Setting, Notes

What are you committed to and honoring through this medicine work?

What did you come to experience?

What do you believe about your healing and your experience with this medicine?

Pure intent means you believe it. What do you intend to shift through this work?

What constructed limitations would you like to address through the medicine? A constructed limitation is like a limiting belief. It's something you believe that is not actually true. For example, believing "I'm not good enough" is limited. In actuality, every single person is made of the same magic with the same potential as another. Therefore, this belief is constructed.

What do you want to grow?

What do you want to curtail?

What will you say when you achieve the healing you desire right now?

During Ceremony, before Medicine

What's the healing you came for?

What are you ready for?

Speak to your higher self, your best friend, your soul. The energy is ready to support you. Help is available because you ask. What will you ask for?

Active Integration through Initial Insights

What visions, feelings, and/or emotional purging occurred during the ceremony and how did it present for you after the ceremony?

Were there parts of the ceremony that were challenging or painful?

What did you learn?

What structures in your life do you want to dissolve as a result of what you experienced?

How will you act on what you learned? Drop information into your heart and hands, and incorporate it into your practical work.

What do you believe as your pure intent now?

Did your belief or intention change?

If there is a change in your belief and/or intention, why do you think that is?

What's next?

Aftercare and Routine Integration

What remembrances or epiphanies came up for you in the week following your ceremony?

Did you experience any physical symptoms or changes in your physical experience?

What are your intentions to continue your healing work?

What commitments do you make to yourself to support your integration over the next 31 days and beyond?

Routine Day 1 Notes

Routine Day 2 Notes

Routine Day 3 Notes

Routine Day 4 Notes

Routine Day 5 Notes

Routine Day 6 Notes

Routine Day 7 Notes

Routine Day 8 Notes

Routine Day 9 Notes

Routine Day 10 Notes

Routine Day 11 Notes

Routine Day 12 Notes

Routine Day 13 Notes

Routine Day 14 Notes

Routine Day 15 Notes

Routine Day 16 Notes

Routine Day 17 Notes

Routine Day 18 Notes

Routine Day 19 Notes

Routine Day 20 Notes

Routine Day 21 Notes

Routine Day 22 Notes

Routine Day 23 Notes

Routine Day 24 Notes

Routine Day 25 Notes

Routine Day 26 Notes

Routine Day 27 Notes

Routine Day 28 Notes

Routine Day 29 Notes

Routine Day 30 Notes

Routine Day 31 Notes

How do you feel about your commitment to the daily actions to support your integration after the ceremony?

Sacred Medicine Community Healing

What is the most valuable experience I can offer to the sacred medicine community?

How can individuals in a sacred medicine community best support me?

Note Pages

Coloring Page

Sketch Page

"A holistic understanding informs many aboriginal wisdom teachings. Like all plant-based Indigenous practices around the world, the use of ayahuasca arises from a tradition where mind and body are seen as inseparable."

— Gabor Maté

Ceremonial Medicine Experience #8

Ceremony Preparation

Scheduled Ceremony Date, Practitioner, Location, Setting, Notes

What are you committed to and honoring through this medicine work?

What did you come to experience?

What do you believe about your healing and your experience with this medicine?

Pure intent means you believe it. What do you intend to shift through this work?

What constructed limitations would you like to address through the medicine? A constructed limitation is like a limiting belief. It's something you believe that is not actually true. For example, believing "I'm not good enough" is limited. In actuality, every single person is made of the same magic with the same potential as another. Therefore, this belief is constructed.

What do you want to grow?

What do you want to curtail?

What will you say when you achieve the healing you desire right now?

During Ceremony, before Medicine

What's the healing you came for?

What are you ready for?

Speak to your higher self, your best friend, your soul. The energy is ready to support you. Help is available because you ask. What will you ask for?

Active Integration through Initial Insights

What visions, feelings, and/or emotional purging occurred during the ceremony and how did it present for you after the ceremony?

Were there parts of the ceremony that were challenging or painful?

What did you learn?

What structures in your life do you want to dissolve as a result of what you experienced?

How will you act on what you learned? Drop information into your heart and hands, and incorporate it into your practical work.

What do you believe as your pure intent now?

Did your belief or intention change?

If there is a change in your belief and/or intention, why do you think that is?

What's next?

Aftercare and Routine Integration

What remembrances or epiphanies came up for you in the week following your ceremony?

Did you experience any physical symptoms or changes in your physical experience?

What are your intentions to continue your healing work?

What commitments do you make to yourself to support your integration over the next 31 days and beyond?

Routine Day 1 Notes

Routine Day 2 Notes

Routine Day 3 Notes

Routine Day 4 Notes

Routine Day 5 Notes

Routine Day 6 Notes

Routine Day 7 Notes

Routine Day 8 Notes

Routine Day 9 Notes

Routine Day 10 Notes

Routine Day 11 Notes

Routine Day 12 Notes

Routine Day 13 Notes

Routine Day 14 Notes

Routine Day 15 Notes

Routine Day 16 Notes

Routine Day 17 Notes

Routine Day 18 Notes

Routine Day 19 Notes

Routine Day 20 Notes

Routine Day 21 Notes

Routine Day 22 Notes

Routine Day 23 Notes

Routine Day 24 Notes

Routine Day 25 Notes

Routine Day 26 Notes

Routine Day 27 Notes

Routine Day 28 Notes

Routine Day 29 Notes

Routine Day 30 Notes

Routine Day 31 Notes

How do you feel about your commitment to the daily actions to support your integration after the ceremony?

Sacred Medicine Community Healing

What is the most valuable experience I can offer to the sacred medicine community?

How can individuals in a sacred medicine community best support me?

Note Pages

Coloring Page

Sketch Page

"If life wasn't real it would be the craziest psychedelic trip ever."

— Joe Rogan

Ceremonial Medicine Experience #9

Ceremony Preparation

Scheduled Ceremony Date, Practitioner, Location, Setting, Notes

What are you committed to and honoring through this medicine work?

What did you come to experience?

What do you believe about your healing and your experience with this medicine?

Pure intent means you believe it. What do you intend to shift through this work?

What constructed limitations would you like to address through the medicine? A constructed limitation is like a limiting belief. It's something you believe that is not actually true. For example, believing "I'm not good enough" is limited. In actuality, every single person is made of the same magic with the same potential as another. Therefore, this belief is constructed.

What do you want to grow?

What do you want to curtail?

What will you say when you achieve the healing you desire right now?

During Ceremony, before Medicine

What's the healing you came for?

What are you ready for?

Speak to your higher self, your best friend, your soul. The energy is ready to support you. Help is available because you ask. What will you ask for?

Active Integration through Initial Insights

What visions, feelings, and/or emotional purging occurred during the ceremony and how did it present for you after the ceremony?

Were there parts of the ceremony that were challenging or painful?

What did you learn?

What structures in your life do you want to dissolve as a result of what you experienced?

How will you act on what you learned? Drop information into your heart and hands, and incorporate it into your practical work.

What do you believe as your pure intent now?

Did your belief or intention change?

If there is a change in your belief and/or intention, why do you think that is?

What's next?

Aftercare and Routine Integration

What remembrances or epiphanies came up for you in the week following your ceremony?

Did you experience any physical symptoms or changes in your physical experience?

What are your intentions to continue your healing work?

What commitments do you make to yourself to support your integration over the next 31 days and beyond?

Routine Day 1 Notes

Routine Day 2 Notes

Routine Day 3 Notes

Routine Day 4 Notes

Routine Day 5 Notes

Routine Day 6 Notes

Routine Day 7 Notes

Routine Day 8 Notes

Routine Day 9 Notes

Routine Day 10 Notes

Routine Day 11 Notes

Routine Day 12 Notes

Routine Day 13 Notes

Routine Day 14 Notes

Routine Day 15 Notes

Routine Day 16 Notes

Routine Day 17 Notes

Routine Day 18 Notes

Routine Day 19 Notes

Routine Day 20 Notes

Routine Day 21 Notes

Routine Day 22 Notes

Routine Day 23 Notes

Routine Day 24 Notes

Routine Day 25 Notes

Routine Day 26 Notes

Routine Day 27 Notes

Routine Day 28 Notes

Routine Day 29 Notes

Routine Day 30 Notes

Routine Day 31 Notes

How do you feel about your commitment to the daily actions to support your integration after the ceremony?

Sacred Medicine Community Healing

What is the most valuable experience I can offer to the sacred medicine community?

How can individuals in a sacred medicine community best support me?

Note Pages

Coloring Page

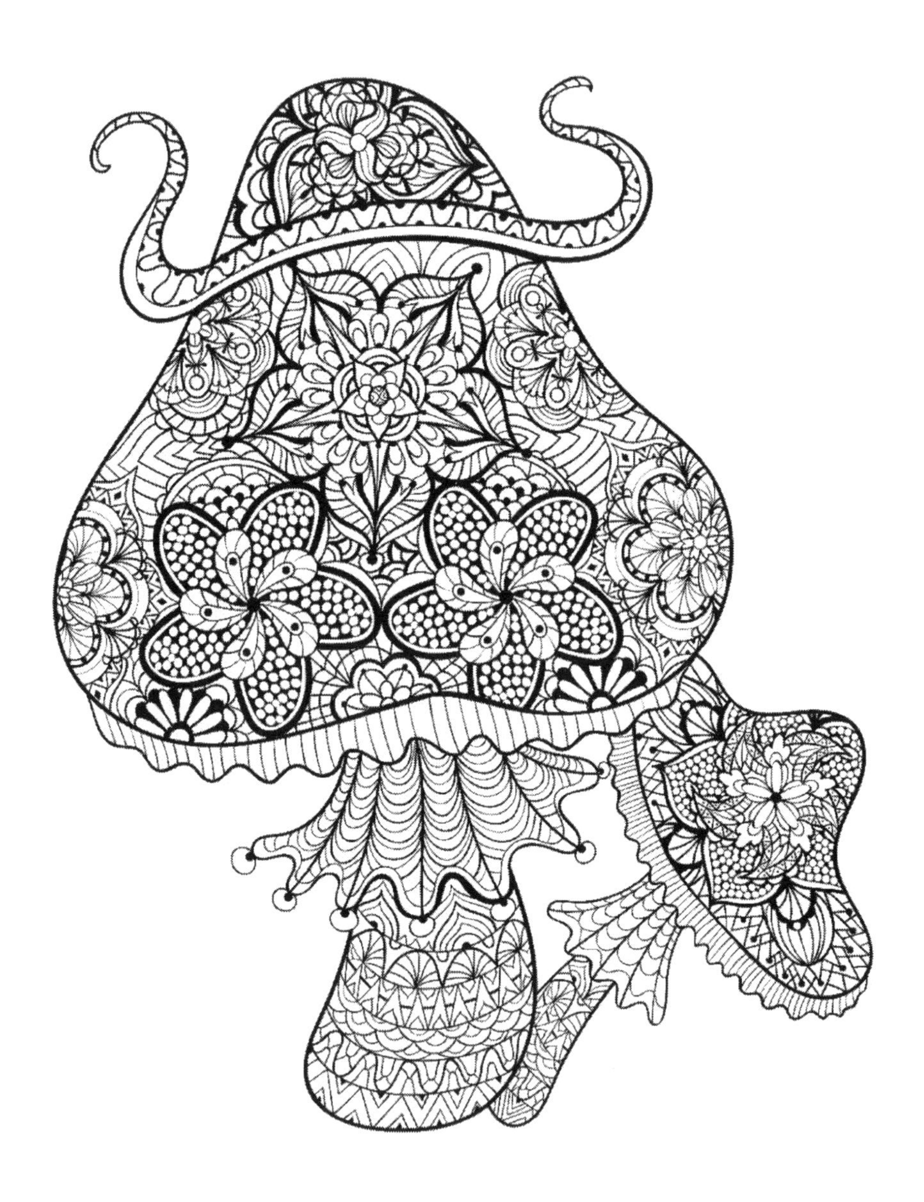

Sketch Page

"There is a wealth of information built into us ... tucked away in the genetic material in every one of our cells ... without some means of access, there is no way even to begin to guess at the extent and quality of what is there. The psychedelic drugs allow exploration of this interior world and insights into its nature."

— Alexander Shulgin

Ceremonial Medicine Experience #10

Ceremony Preparation

Scheduled Ceremony Date, Practitioner, Location, Setting, Notes

What are you committed to and honoring through this medicine work?

What did you come to experience?

What do you believe about your healing and your experience with this medicine?

Pure intent means you believe it. What do you intend to shift through this work?

What constructed limitations would you like to address through the medicine? A constructed limitation is like a limiting belief. It's something you believe that is not actually true. For example, believing "I'm not good enough" is limited. In actuality, every single person is made of the same magic with the same potential as another. Therefore, this belief is constructed.

What do you want to grow?

What do you want to curtail?

What will you say when you achieve the healing you desire right now?

During Ceremony, before Medicine

What's the healing you came for?

What are you ready for?

Speak to your higher self, your best friend, your soul. The energy is ready to support you. Help is available because you ask. What will you ask for?

Active Integration through Initial Insights

What visions, feelings, and/or emotional purging occurred during the ceremony and how did it present for you after the ceremony?

Were there parts of the ceremony that were challenging or painful?

What did you learn?

What structures in your life do you want to dissolve as a result of what you experienced?

How will you act on what you learned? Drop information into your heart and hands, and incorporate it into your practical work.

What do you believe as your pure intent now?

Did your belief or intention change?

If there is a change in your belief and/or intention, why do you think that is?

What's next?

Aftercare and Routine Integration

What remembrances or epiphanies came up for you in the week following your ceremony?

Did you experience any physical symptoms or changes in your physical experience?

What are your intentions to continue your healing work?

What commitments do you make to yourself to support your integration over the next 31 days and beyond?

Routine Day 1 Notes

Routine Day 2 Notes

Routine Day 3 Notes

Routine Day 4 Notes

Routine Day 5 Notes

Routine Day 6 Notes

Routine Day 7 Notes

Routine Day 8 Notes

Routine Day 9 Notes

Routine Day 10 Notes

Routine Day 11 Notes

Routine Day 12 Notes

Routine Day 13 Notes

Routine Day 14 Notes

Routine Day 15 Notes

Routine Day 16 Notes

Routine Day 17 Notes

Routine Day 18 Notes

Routine Day 19 Notes

Routine Day 20 Notes

Routine Day 21 Notes

Routine Day 22 Notes

Routine Day 23 Notes

Routine Day 24 Notes

Routine Day 25 Notes

Routine Day 26 Notes

Routine Day 27 Notes

Routine Day 28 Notes

Routine Day 29 Notes

Routine Day 30 Notes

Routine Day 31 Notes

How do you feel about your commitment to the daily actions to support your integration after the ceremony?

Sacred Medicine Community Healing

What is the most valuable experience I can offer to the sacred medicine community?

How can individuals in a sacred medicine community best support me?

Note Pages

Coloring Page

Sketch Page

"To be empowered, to be free, to be unlimited,

to be creative, to be genius, to be divine -

that is who you are."

— Dr. Joe Dispenza

Ceremonial Medicine Experience #11

Ceremony Preparation

Scheduled Ceremony Date, Practitioner, Location, Setting, Notes

What are you committed to and honoring through this medicine work?

What did you come to experience?

What do you believe about your healing and your experience with this medicine?

Pure intent means you believe it. What do you intend to shift through this work?

What constructed limitations would you like to address through the medicine? A constructed limitation is like a limiting belief. It's something you believe that is not actually true. For example, believing "I'm not good enough" is limited. In actuality, every single person is made of the same magic with the same potential as another. Therefore, this belief is constructed.

What do you want to grow?

What do you want to curtail?

What will you say when you achieve the healing you desire right now?

During Ceremony, before Medicine

What's the healing you came for?

What are you ready for?

Speak to your higher self, your best friend, your soul. The energy is ready to support you. Help is available because you ask. What will you ask for?

Active Integration through Initial Insights

What visions, feelings, and/or emotional purging occurred during the ceremony and how did it present for you after the ceremony?

Were there parts of the ceremony that were challenging or painful?

What did you learn?

What structures in your life do you want to dissolve as a result of what you experienced?

How will you act on what you learned? Drop information into your heart and hands, and incorporate it into your practical work.

What do you believe as your pure intent now?

Did your belief or intention change?

If there is a change in your belief and/or intention, why do you think that is?

What's next?

Aftercare and Routine Integration

What remembrances or epiphanies came up for you in the week following your ceremony?

Did you experience any physical symptoms or changes in your physical experience?

What are your intentions to continue your healing work?

What commitments do you make to yourself to support your integration over the next 31 days and beyond?

Routine Day 1 Notes

Routine Day 2 Notes

Routine Day 3 Notes

Routine Day 4 Notes

Routine Day 5 Notes

Routine Day 6 Notes

Routine Day 7 Notes

Routine Day 8 Notes

Routine Day 9 Notes

Routine Day 10 Notes

Routine Day 11 Notes

Routine Day 12 Notes

Routine Day 13 Notes

Routine Day 14 Notes

Routine Day 15 Notes

Routine Day 16 Notes

Routine Day 17 Notes

Routine Day 18 Notes

Routine Day 19 Notes

Routine Day 20 Notes

Routine Day 21 Notes

Routine Day 22 Notes

Routine Day 23 Notes

Routine Day 24 Notes

Routine Day 25 Notes

Routine Day 26 Notes

Routine Day 27 Notes

Routine Day 28 Notes

Routine Day 29 Notes

Routine Day 30 Notes

Routine Day 31 Notes

How do you feel about your commitment to the daily actions to support your integration after the ceremony?

Sacred Medicine Community Healing

What is the most valuable experience I can offer to the sacred medicine community?

How can individuals in a sacred medicine community best support me?

Note Pages

Coloring Page

Sketch Page

"Do the work to keep the lines open.

Do the work to reach out to communities.

Don't rely on just one group to do it,

everyone has a role to play in the shaping

of this [psychedelic] movement."

— Amy Emerson

Community Support

Suggested Communities

Integration Mentors Melissa and Mayra have a Facebook group, Collaborative AF Healing, where like-minded people connect and discuss their healing journey. Here, you'll find daily encouragement, content, events, and culture, all curated for the wounded healer's journey. Melissa and Mayra also offer a Brilliant Transformation program to supplement plant medicine work. A Brilliant Transformation helps you emerge as the butterfly—restoring you to the person you were born to be and supporting your continued growth and healing. We will address the soul of your life experience through a series of coaching sessions and NLP processes. Together, we'll evaluate your values, eliminate negative emotions, rewire traumatic experiences, remove and transition limiting beliefs, integrate conflicting parts, and install your new vision and values.

The following team prepared this sacred medicine companion journal to support your medicine journey. They are standing by to assist with your ongoing integration and ceremonial needs.

Integration Mentors

Melissa Drake is an intuitive life coach and NLP practitioner with a BA in Business Management. As an author, TEDx Speaker, and entrepreneur, Melissa helps individuals connect, collaborate, and heal through personal stories and experiences. Having personally endured many of life's toughest transitions, Melissa turned to plant medicine to facilitate greater personal and generational healing. She is keenly aware of trauma and the role writing and movement—specifically dance—play in one's recovery. She's a compassionate listener, solutions-based resource, and mystic midwife to help you pursue your dreams and go further than you could go alone. You can reach her at melissa@uncorpedinfluence.com.

Mayra Aceves is a in Neuro Design Engineer and Transformational Hypnotist with a BA in Social Science and background in education. She's a mother of four and a continual seeker of growth and transformation who is always learning and evolving. Her mission is to continue creating a space for connection through collective collaboration, healing, and ultimate transformation, while providing the tools necessary to maximize all peaks of transformation, through Neuro-linguistic rewiring, hypnotherapy, coaching, and ice bath therapy. You can reach her at maceves7779@gmail.com.

Ceremonial Plant Medicine Practitioners

Jonathan Anderson is a Bufo Alvarius and Kambo practitioner as well as a student of ceremonial plant medicine on the path of medicine and spirituality since the age of 18. Quickly plant medicine became a way of life for Jonathan and his family as well. He started leading ceremonies at the age of 23 and continues to participate in ceremonies with great elders. Jonathan spends much time connecting to his family's lineage from Colombia and being surrounded by nature as much as possible. Martial arts and physical movement are of great importance to him. On the path and mission to alleviate the worlds suffering, he uses sacred medicine to curate the greatest conscious shifts possible while spreading love and light unto all. You can reach him at mamicajo97@gmail.com.

Eden Rincon is a reiki and energy healer, who assists and participates in plant medicine ceremonies, and has been playing instruments since the age of eight. She spends her time hiking, connecting with nature, painting, playing music and making the world a better place. She is on a mission to embrace, unify, and spread the potent power of love to others and the universe. You can reach her at rincon.eden@yahoo.com.

Customize the Journal and Support Your Community

We are happy to share that a free single-use journal is available as a download at bit.ly/IntegrationDownload.

In addition, the single-use journal is available to healers, plant medicine practitioners, shamans, and integration mentors who wish to license the content. Our team will collaborate with you to create a branded version of the journal to promote your own ceremonial medicine experiences and integration services. Supply your own cover, or pick from our pre-designed options, or collaboratively create something new.

Printed and digital versions of the single-use journal can be used to supplement retreats and ceremonial gatherings.

For greater support and client management, we also offer a done-for-you, personalized ecosystem to collect email addresses and communicate with and support individuals throughout their ceremonial medicine experience and integration journey.

Please email melissa@uncorpedinfluence.com for details.

"la alegría siempre acompaña !

Bienvenidos a pensar Bonito para ser feliz."

(Joy always accompanies!

Welcome to think beautiful to be happy.)

— Taita Cesar Lezama

Resources

Other Books from the Authors

Melissa Drake, *TranscenDANCE: Letting the Universe Lead*

Melissa Drake, *The Orgasmic Entrepreneur: Discover the Sweet Spot of Love, Sex, and Business by Simply Being YOU*

Referenced Books and Recommended Reading

Katherine E. Coder, PhD., *After the Ceremony Ends: A Companion Guide to Help You Integrate Visionary Plant Medicine Experiences*

Joe Dispenza, *Breaking the Habit of Being Yourself: How to Lose Your Mind and Create a New One*

Napoleon Hill, *Outwitting the Devil: The Secret to Freedom and Success*

Robin Wall Kimmerer, *Braiding Sweetgrass: Indigenous Wisdom, Scientific Knowledge and the Teachings of Plants*

Vishen Lakhiani, *The Buddha and the Badass: The Secret Spiritual Art of Succeeding at Work*

Jose Manik Ajpu Munoz, *Butterflies: Memories Through Space and Time*

Michael Pollan, *How to Change Your Mind: What the New Science of Psychedelics Teaches Us About Consciousness, Dying, Addiction, Depression, and Transcendence*

William Richards, *Sacred Knowledge: Psychedelics and Religious Experiences*

Don Miguel Ruiz, *The Four Agreements: A Practical Guide to Personal Freedom (A Toltec Wisdom Book)*

Don Miguel Ruiz, *The Mastery of Love: A Practical Guide to the Art of Relationship: A Toltec Wisdom Book*

Don Miguel Ruiz, *The Mastery of Self: A Toltec Guide to Personal Freedom*

Joseph Tafur MD, *The Fellowship of the River: A Medical Doctor's Exploration into Traditional Amazonian Plant*

Charles T. Tart, *Altered states of Consciousness*

Playlists

Because music and movement are amazing integration tools, we've created three different playlists to soundtrack your ceremonial medicine and integration experience.

Ceremony, bit.ly/MedicineCeremony
This playlist includes mellow and contemplative tunes—perfect for reflection, introspection, surrender, and release.

Journey Through Sound, bit.ly/CeremonySoundJourney
Curated by Dee Jay MJ, this playlist includes a diverse set that's inspired by ceremonial journeys.

The Orgasmic Entrepreneur, bit.ly/OrgasmicEntrepreneurPlaylist
This playlist contains songs related to being one's true self, including being centered, connected, fun, and a bit rebellious.

Ultimate Vida, bit.ly/UltimateVidaPlaylist
This playlist contains songs that inspire you to live your best life—one that's free, connected, and prosperous.

When the integration process can be as equally respected as our desires for expanded states or mystical experiences, the wisdom and maturity of an awakening soul has dawned.

— Matt Kahn

Made in the USA
Monee, IL
26 September 2022

43a686c5-ac48-4f3d-a5ca-a0a7bf3e4c8aR01